THIS BOOK
BELONGS TO...

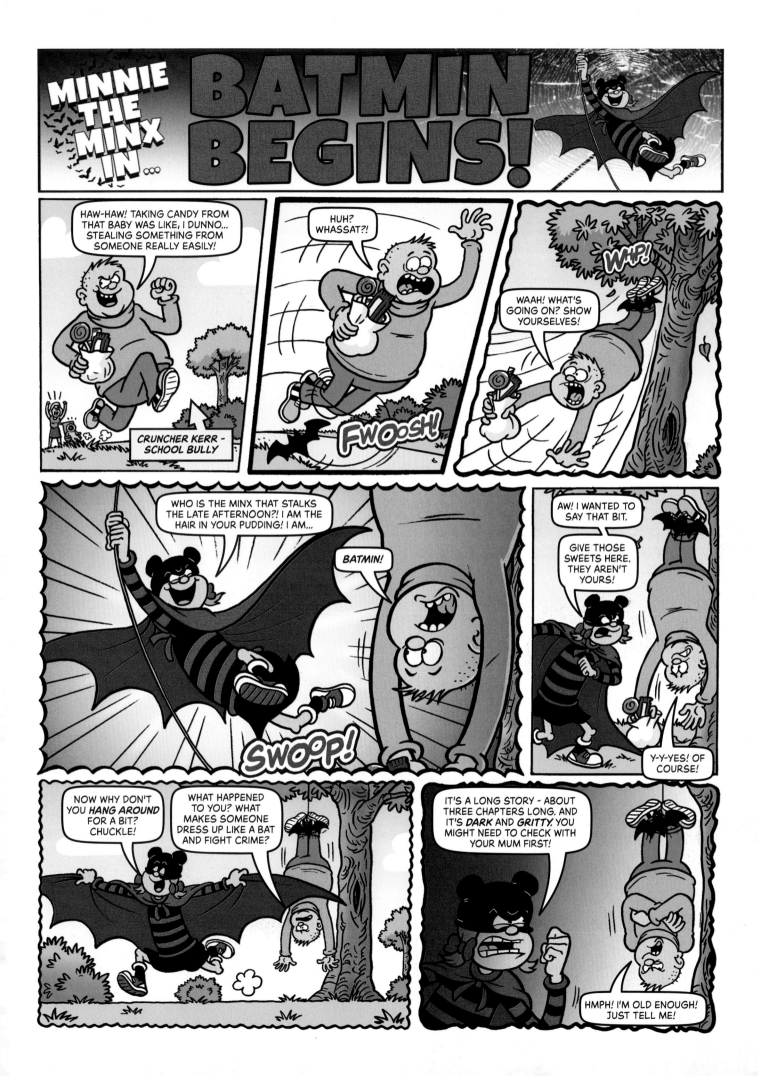

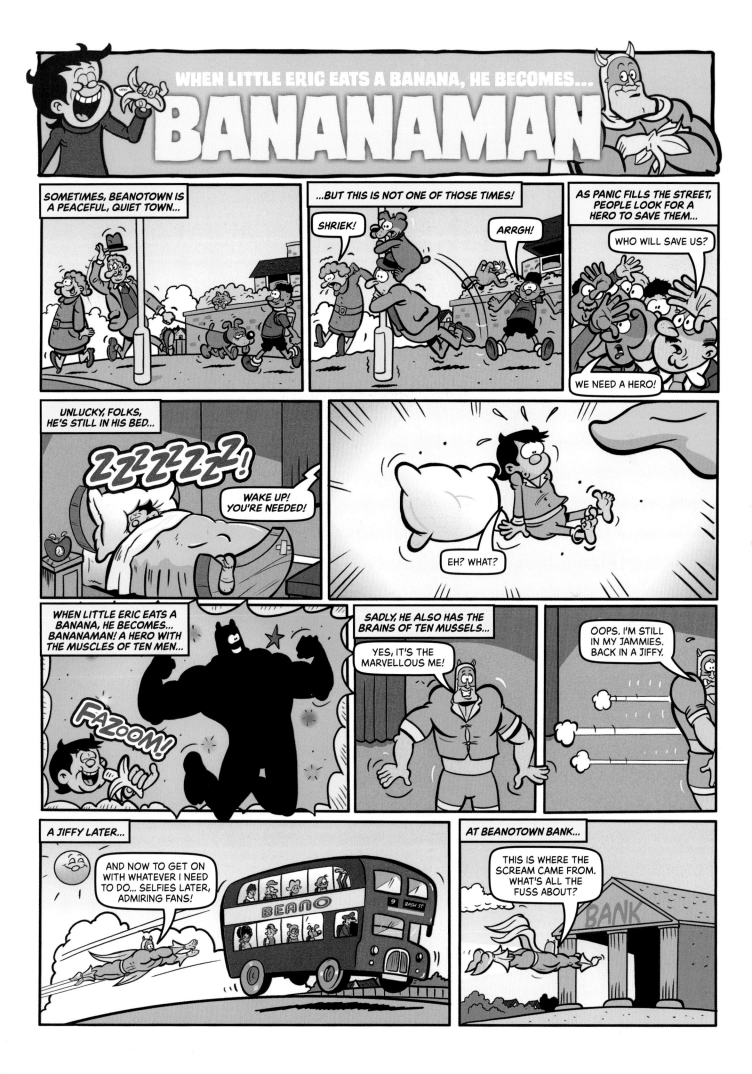

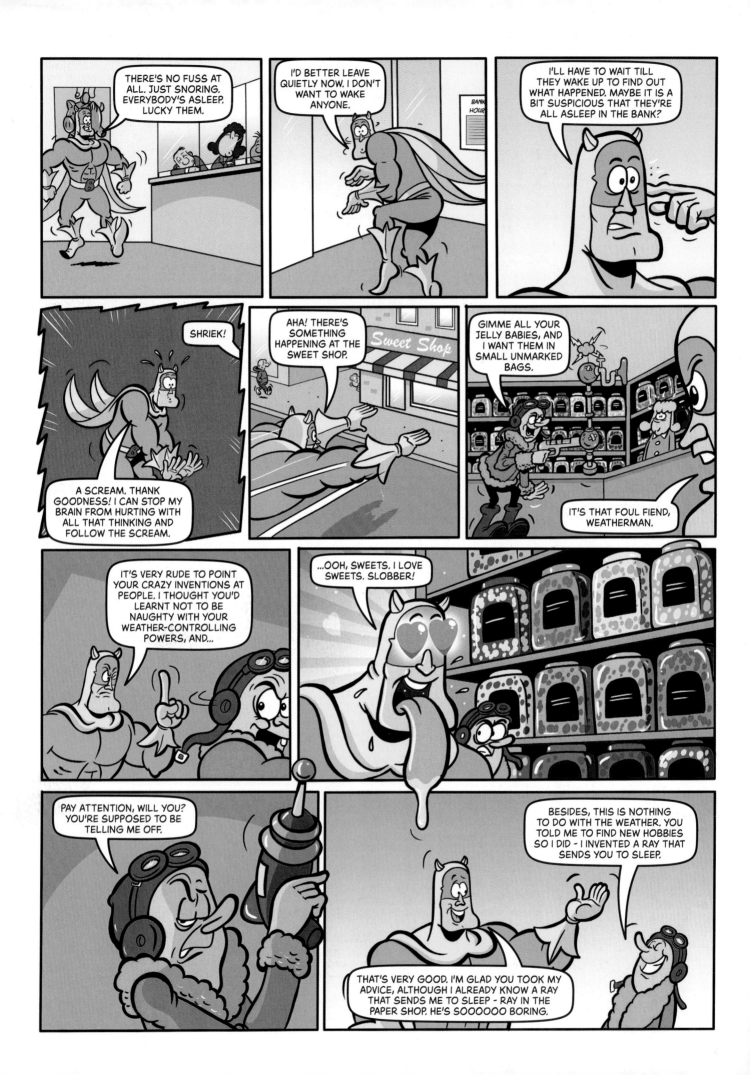

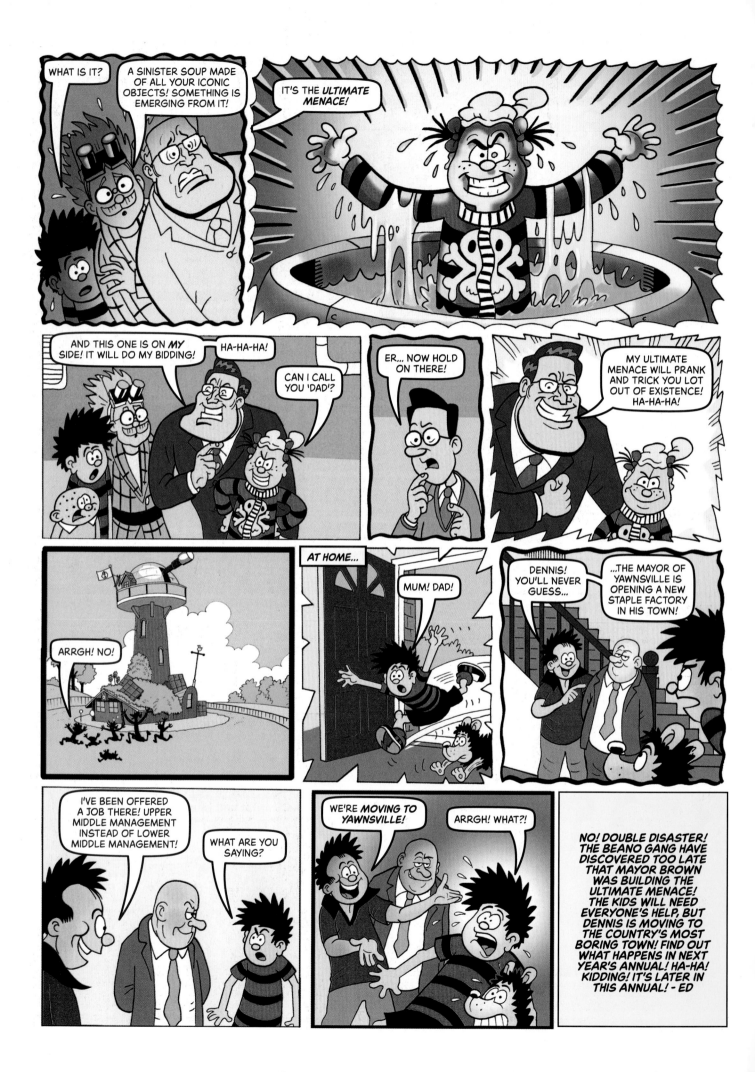

SUPERHERO SCHOOL!

Have you got what it takes to be a superhero like Batmin?
Find your own superpowers with this awesome trick!

LESSON 2

HOW TO MAKE STUFF FLOAT!

WHAT YOU'LL NEED
- A pencil or chopstick
- A piece of paper

WHAT TO DO

1 Hide a pencil up your arm by clasping it with your pinkie. Make sure nobody can see it.

2 Take a sheet of paper and hold it up for your audience to see.

3 Move your hands into the centre of your body and scrunch up the paper, pressing the pencil into your body as you do. Keep the pencil hidden.

4 Scrunch the paper as tightly as you can. Lay the pencil over your left hand like this, making sure you do this at the person's eye level so they don't see the pencil, only the ball of paper.

THIS IS YOUR HOMEWORK, MINNIE!

5 Place your right hand above the ball of paper and press down on the pencil with the palm of your hand like this, all the time making sure the pencil is hidden from your audience.

6 Press down slowly on the end of the pencil and the paper ball will begin to rise and look like it's floating!

SWALLOWED A FLY!

Help Rubi shrink all the things Pie Face has shot with the grow-bigger ray by finding them in this wordsearch!

O	F	R	S	A	C	T	D	O	G
L	H	I	O	T	G	R	S	R	S
D	Y	B	A	N	N	L	K	P	T
W	O	C	T	R	E	Q	M	N	R
O	S	H	O	R	S	E	R	Y	I
M	H	F	D	X	E	Z	A	L	N
A	B	L	M	J	G	D	P	U	G
N	G	F	R	E	Q	C	I	A	V
R	F	D	M	N	L	K	P	P	O
E	D	F	L	Y	S	A	Q	U	S

TICK 'EM OFF AS YOU FIND THEM!

- FLY ☐
- SPIDER ☐
- CAT ☐
- DOG ☐
- COW ☐
- HORSE ☐
- STRING ☐
- PAUL ☐
- OLD WOMAN ☐

🔍 **Solution**

BETTY AND THE YETI!

THE ORDINARY GIRL WITH THE EXTRAORDINARY BEST FRIEND!

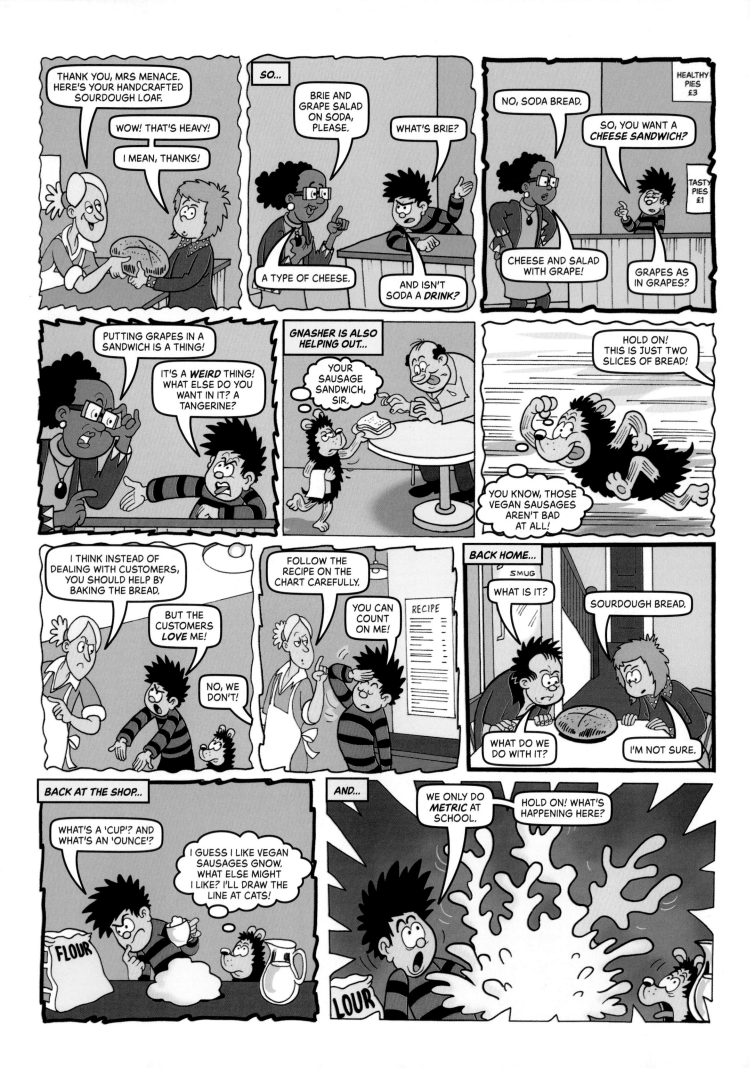

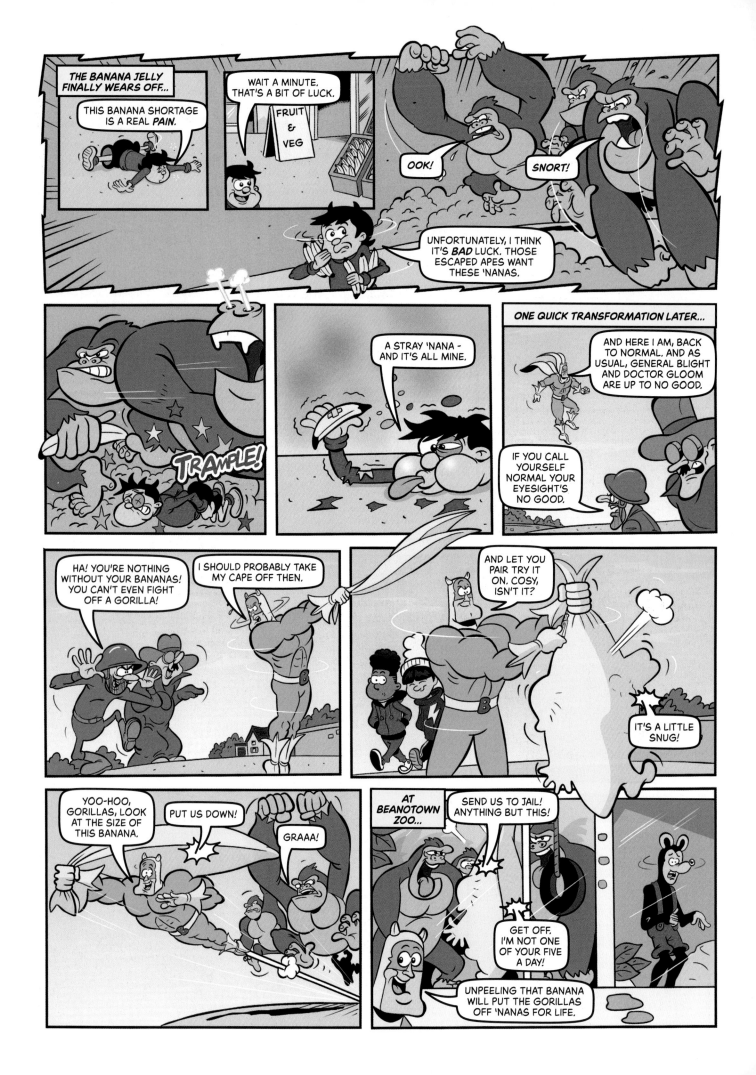

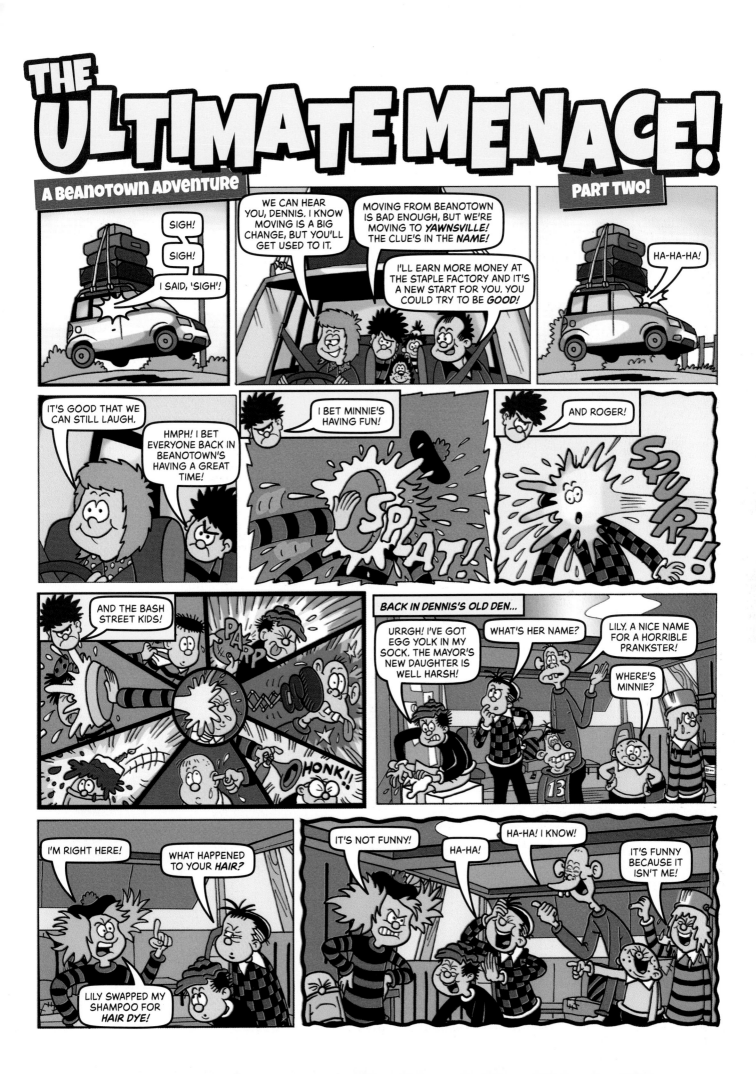

UNIFORMLY DIFFERENT!

Can you spot the differences between these two shots of the kids at the police station? There are ten changes to spot.

Q **Solution**

Smiffy's tie, 'Erbert's shoes, Sidney's jumper, Spotty's tie, Plug's hat, Danny's jumper, Fatty's blazer, Wilf's jumper, Wilf's comb, Toots's jumper.